Othello

3

Satomi Ikezawa

TRANSLATED AND ADAPTED BY
William Flanagan

LETTERED BY
Michaelis/Carpelis Design

tanoshimi

LONDON

Published in the United Kingdom by Tanoshimi in 2007

1 3 5 7 9 10 8 6 4 2

Othello Volume 3 is a work of fiction. Names, characters, places and incidents are the products of the
author's imagination or are used fictitiously. Any resemblance to actual events, locales, or
persons, living or dead, is entirely coincidental.

First published in Japan in 2003 by Kodansha Ltd., Tokyo

Published by arrangement with Kodansha Ltd., Tokyo and with Del Rey,
an imprint of Random House Inc., New York

Tanoshimi
Random House, 20 Vauxhall Bridge Road,
London, SW1V 2SA

www.tanoshimi.tv
www.randomhouse.co.uk

Addresses for companies within The Random House Group Limited can be found at:
www.randomhouse.co.uk/offices.htm

The Random House Group Limited Reg. No. 954009

A CIP catalogue record for this book is available from the British Library

ISBN 9780099506492

The Random House Group Limited makes every effort to ensure that the papers used in its books are made
from trees that have been legally sourced from well-managed and credibly certified forests. Our paper
procurement policy can be found at: www.randomhouse.co.uk/paper.htm

Printed and bound in Germany by GGP Media GmbH, Pößneck

Translator and adaptor — William Flanagan
Lettering — Michaelis/Carpelis Design

Contents

Honorifics

Throughout the Tanoshimi Manga books, you will find Japanese honorifics left intact in the translations. For those not familiar with how the Japanese use honorifics, and more importantly, how they differ from English honorifics, we present this brief overview.

Politeness has always been a critical facet of Japanese culture. Ever since the feudal era, when Japan was a highly stratified society, use of honorifics—which can be defined as polite speech that indicates relationship or status—has played an essential role in the Japanese language. When addressing someone in Japanese, an honorific usually takes the form of a suffix attached to one's name (example: 'Asuna-san'), or as a title at the end of one's name or in place of the name itself (example: 'Negi-sensei,' or simply 'Sensei!').

Honorifics can be expressions of respect or endearment. In the context of manga and anime, honorifics give insight into the nature of the relationship between characters. Many translations into English leave out these important honorifics, and therefore distort the 'feel' of the original Japanese. Because Japanese honorifics contain nuances that English honorifics lack, it is our policy at Tanoshimi not to translate them. Here, instead, is a guide to some of the honorifics you may encounter in Tanoshimi Manga.

-san: This is the most common honorific, and is equivalent to Mr., Miss, Ms., Mrs., etc. It is the all-purpose honorific and can be used in any situation where politeness is required.

-sama: This is one level higher than '-san.' It is used to confer great respect.

-dono: This comes from the word 'tono,' which means 'lord.' It is even a higher level than '-sama,' and confers utmost respect.

-kun: This suffix is used at the end of boys' names to express familiarity or endearment. It is also sometimes used by men amongst friends, or when addressing someone younger or of a lower station.

-chan: This is used to express endearment, mostly towards girls. It is also used for little boys, pets, and even among lovers. It gives a sense of childish cuteness.

Bozu: This is an informal way to refer to a boy, similar to the English terms "kid".

Sempai: This title suggests that the addressee is one's 'senior' in a group or organization. It is most often used in a school setting, where underclassmen refer to their upperclassmen as 'sempai.' It can also be used in the workplace, such as when a newer employee addresses an employee who has seniority in the company.

Kohai: This is the opposite of '-sempai,' and is used towards underclassmen in school or newcomers in the workplace. It connotes that the addressee is of lower station.

Sensei: Literally meaning 'one who has come before,' this title is used for teachers, doctors, or masters of any profession or art.

[blank]: Usually forgotten in these lists, but perhaps the most significant difference between Japanese and English. The lack of honorific means that the speaker has permission to address the person in a very intimate way. Usually, only family, spouses, or very close friends have this kind of permission. Known as *yobisute*, it can be gratifying when someone who has earned the intimacy starts to call one by one's name without an honorific. But when that intimacy hasn't been earned, it can also be very insulting.

A Note from the Author

When I draw about the live music scene, my workplace starts to look like a rehearsal studio! Guitar case, mike stands, effects equipment, etc. The very limited airspace is taken up with musical instruments and other music stuff! An assistant decided which case would be perfect to carry a guitar. If we only had drums and amps, we'd be ready for a live performance!

OTHELLO

OTHELLO
オセロ。

Satomi Ikezawa

3

Are you crying yourself to sleep from all the awful things that happen?
Well, don't! It's bad for your health.
The best thing for a time like that is...

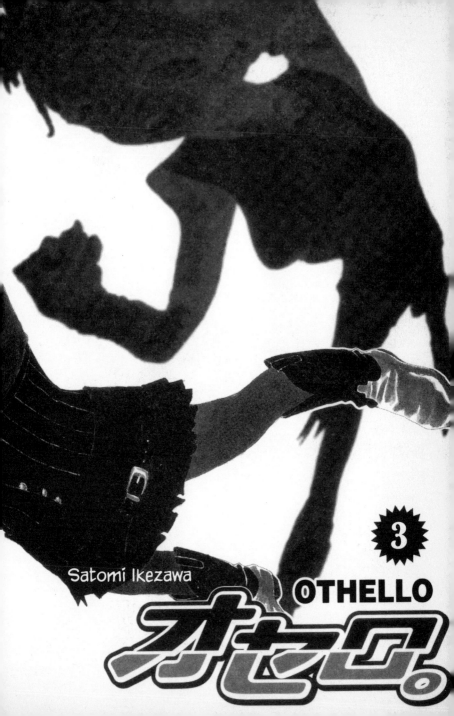

Satomi Ikezawa

OTHELLO

3

オセロ。

Justice
is done!!

Chapter 9
Could Never Forget

Yaya...

Moriyama...kun...

Nana appeared at the outdoor live performance of Moriyama's band, but in the rain, Moriyama received an electric shock which takes out his voice. In an effort to help him, Nana sings the vocals for the band, and the power of her performance wins over the crowd. However, before she finishes, she receives an electric shock herself, and returns to the Yaya personality. Suddenly, when timid Yaya realizes she is on stage, she faints! Moriyama, who witnessed the Yaya/Nana transformation, becomes aware that Yaya and Nana are in fact the same person. Nana also tells Moriyama that Nana knows all about Yaya, but Yaya doesn't know about Nana. Moriyama, understanding the trouble that Yaya could be in, decides that he will protect Yaya.

Nana's on a rampage, and Yaya doesn't know!!

オセロ。

The Story Thus Far

And just who is to blame for that, Shingyôji-san?

Who?

This is rehearsal time! My band is already in Yoyogi Park waiting for us!

Heh. I never knew you were so petty, Moriyama.

After all, it is only an hour!

You are!!

You're a whole hour late!!

And your cell phone is turned off!

You suggested that you'd like to come because you had free time!

It wasn't me inviting you!

I promised you that I'd attend this dull rehearsal of yours, and I will!

You should *thank* me!

Don't get so angry!

STARE
じ″

...

Anyway, we have to hurry!

Huh? Shingyôji-san?

STOMP STOMP

...absolutely refuse to cross *that* bridge.

My legs...

It worries me.

I have an aura that projects from my body...

Don't worry! Nobody will notice! You're Shingyôji-san now!

Hm. I'm not so sure...

It would have been better to come by the Shibuya side!

MUMBLE MUMBLE

MUMBLE

If we don't cross that bridge, we'll never get to Yoyogi Park.

.....

Moriyama, you're as cold as ice!

Then stay there and worry for the rest of your life.

I'll go alone.

I-I'm sorry! I'm just not feeling well enough for this today.

Maybe it's a cold.

This is called: having trouble saying no to the endless requests for poses.

Th-This is scary!

HUH?

Let me give you a hand, Mimi. Down we go.

I'm sorry! I was asking too much!

Th-There was a guy like that?

I only saw Moriyama-kun.

○oo

← Left out.

KYAA KYAA
KYAA
きゃ きゃ きゃ ♥ ♥
きゅん♥
きゃ ♥

Me too!

Aww! I wanted to see his face without those sunglasses!

Shingyôji-san, what did you think of that arrangement?

.....

Well...

ぷっ FFF

かあ HAA .:

It's okay, I guess.

Sigh

Yeah...

Let's take a break, huh?

.....

GRIN

That girl who jumped on stage during your live performance...

I find her interesting.

AH!

N-No. Nothing.

Huh?

Ha ha! If you're looking for her, you just met--

Hm. Nana. I'd like to meet her.

Oh, you mean Nana?

What's that reaction for? Is she your girlfriend?

Eh?!

Then introduce me!

"Couldn't say"? You know her, don't you?

I-I couldn't say...

What kind of girl is she?

No, she isn't...

More or less. We're in the same class at school...

SKRRCH

POINNG

Y... Yeah...fine.

Forgive me. Are you all right?

Thank you.

Yeah...f-- Ah! Over there! ♡

Can you direct me to the lunch counter?

Yeah... fine. ♡

Are you on lunch break?

Hey lady, I want a Yaki-soba sandwich, a croquette sandwich and a curry sandwich!

I was first!

KYAAA

GWAAAAR

Hey, don't push!

YAAA YAAA

I wanted to bump into him!!

Who the heck was that? He was too cool!

Yes, I can die now!

MELT MELT

What a waste!

He's pretty!

—27—

—31—

I'm not the kind of girl who would raise a fuss for the sake of one little anpan bun.

...ut you ...aised a ...g fuss ...ready!

Ha! Since you admit your guilt, I'll let you go.

F-Forgive me!

Forgive me!

BONK

ぽむッ

.....

I've taken pity on you. Take this.

...Nana!

I've found you...

—45—

Chapter 10
Declaration
of War

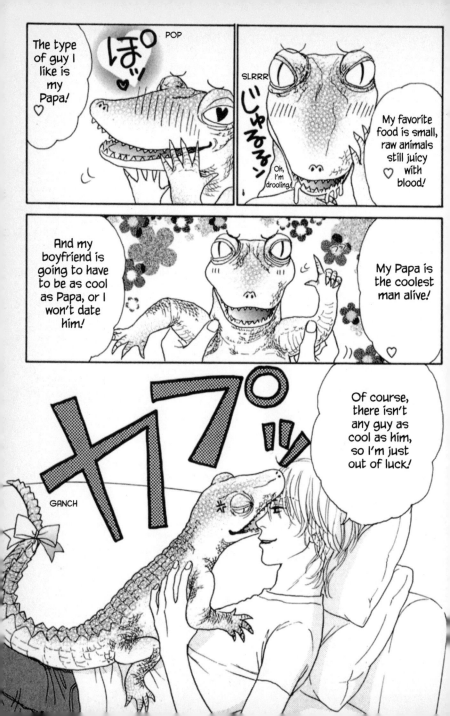

...to change her mind about me?

So how do I get Nana...

It looks like I'll actually have to get serious about work.

BURP

Because I wasn't able to work as staff at your recent live performance.

It's really unforgivable.

Huh? Why?

Say, Moriyama -kun...

I should go and apologize to the members of Black Dog.

Huh? What?

Oh, nothing.

There's nothing to apologize for! Don't give it a second thought!

Oh yeah, between the time she got there and the performance, she changed from Yaya to Nana.

Okay.

......

Please! Let me know when you're rehearsing next?

I have to! Otherwise I'd just feel guilty!

I know this is a bad habit of mine...

I can't! This is too scary!

...but I can only see bad things happening!

Studio B1

"Who are you, anyway?"

"We've got no use for people we can't trust!"

"What's the use in apologizing now?"

Humph!

Gather up your courage, and put one foot in front of the other, Yaya!

It's my imagination! Reality won't go that way!

SHAKE ぶん ぶん SHAKE

Giving away stuff given me by a weirdo like him seems almost like trafficking in black-market items.

Sure, I can vouch for the taste, but...

Do musicians even like anpan buns?

And these anpan buns that guy gave me might have had something weird done to them...

Nana-chan, at your service!

Not my best entrance, but...

Oh, here! A gift of the best anpan buns in Japan (according to some).

I'm just fine! I just came to hang with you guys!

It looks like it hurts!

You're cut! Are you okay?

Huh? It was you, Nana-chan?!

What's the difference?

Ha ha ha ha!

There's a big difference!

GRR

VK-y

Mainly because Yaya wanted to come, and you show up instead.

What is it, Moriyama? You look like you have a complaint.

HUMPH!

Don't want any.

Huh? There's plenty for you, too.

They look great!!

A little squished, but...

Hold it, Furuta-kun! You don't have the right to make that offer yet!

Ah ha ha! You'll make my head spin!

You got a sweet voice, your rhythm instinct is right on target, and you got lungs that won't quit!

I want all that working for *us*!!

Nana-chan! I'm serious! Come join our band!

What he said!

.....

Sorry for the wait.

Ohhh!

I-I was joking, you know...

It's just one of my many hobbies.

No!! Don't you see this apron?

GRR

Ah ha ha! It looks like it, right?

You don't have some old granny as live-in help, do you? Ha ha ha!

Aw! I wanted to show off my knowledge, but they're not interested, huh?

Heh. My lecture would lose you anyway.

Thank you, Sensei!

But you can skip the lecture! Just pour the wine!

This wine is sure to be wasted on people like you, but I'll open it for the special occasion.

They say this wine is unusually good.

↑ He just wanted an excuse to drink it.

CHINNK カイーンッ

Now... Kampai!!

What's odd? I simply made a present of the very thing you wanted.

Ah, the bouquet develops.

But normally you don't buy every bun in the shop.

AH HA HA!

But I must say that our shopping trip for anpan buns...

...was a very odd affair, Shingyôji-san.

SKRRT カバタ

How nice for them.

It's against my policy to wedge myself between two people.

Ah ha ha!

.....

You don't?

No! Isn't it obvious?

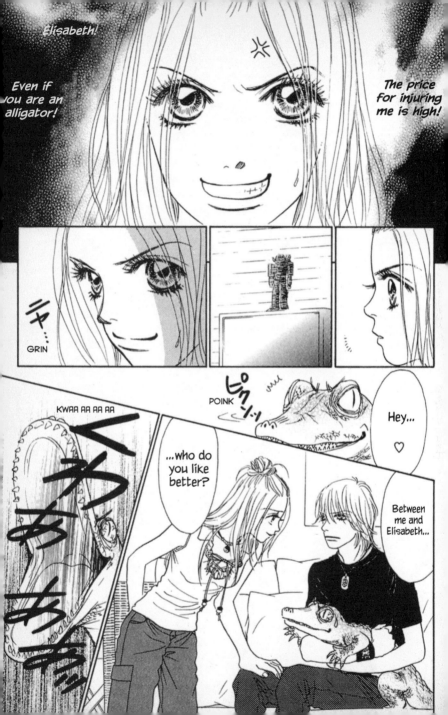

GUWAAAAAAMP

Nana is a little scary.

I knew it already, and still I'm scared.

Ahhh! That felt good!

Time for a good drink!

By the way, Shingyôji-san...

...I figured it out.

You're Shôhei from Juliet, right?

..... Hm.

So I let my secret out?

My aura gave me away.

The only thing I'll say is, there was one person I could not get along with.

I'll leave that to your imagination.

.....

Was it those internal band arguments you always hear about?

Why did you guys break up?

In the end, it will happen. You will be made mine!

Nana...

I've been drawn in by that aspect of yours. I'm caught and I won't be let go.

The day of the gig...

...you'll be there as Nana, won't you?

Oh!

That's right, Nana! Will you be all right?

What about?

What happens on the day if you don't change into Nana?

That'd be awful! That'd be terrible!

w-- "Work out"? Worry a little, will ya?

You sure?

It'll be fahn! Jes' fahn!

Just fine!

...ause I'm ...ared.

HA HA HA HAAAAH

Aw, it'll all work out!

Eh?!

I could hand out flyers or take tickets... Anything, just let me help!

If I've got Nana as a guest singer and Yaya as staff, that means...

It's a double booking!!

...it's almost as if...

You can't do that!!

I see...

We're all set for staff on this gig.

Uh... I mean ...

Huh? I can't?

That's it!

Th-Then at least let me come to apologize. I'll bring a gift and--

You don't have to come at all!!

Hey! Hey, Moriyama...

BYE-BYE!

Sorry. I'm in a hurry...

"I'm here for you..."

"It'll be all right. I'm here for you."

But I can't just go and tell Yaya the truth!

That was pretty cold of me.

Dammit! I ended up telling a big lie!

Mm...

I guess we should start rehearsal, huh?

Heh heh.

I told you so. She blew us off.

That's not decided yet.

SIGH

ホゥ…

Your face doesn't say "nothing."

Neither do your sighs.

Oh... Nothing.

What's wrong, Mimi?

I don't have the courage to go.

He might like me even less if I did.

You're kidding!

Then the last place you should be is here!

I wanted to see the guy I like at a performance today.

.....

Really? Then you'd better get there quick!

Your favorite band's set might end before you get there!

It's okay.

I know where it is.

Oh...I--I'm sorry...

I think you have the wrong club.

The Nanameikan is on the other side of the station.

What am I doing? I'm an idiot! I'm such a coward!

Th-- Thank you!

BOW

BOW

Take care, okay?

BUMP

I should just go home tonight.

Kyaa!

But I stand out too much in this outfit.

It may distract Moriyama, too

What's so good about this guy?

..... Huh?

I get it! He doesn't recognize me through my makeup.

N-- No, I'm fine...

It looks like you're not hurt either.

They're done as a band, right? How long do you plan to keep hanging on?

Juliet? I can't help but wonder about you.

OTHELLO PRODUSED BY S.T
RAKUSHOBROTHERS INC.

BLUSSH

Ha ha! You have a point.

W-What gives you the right to question my hobbies?

But...

Kyaa!

.....

Wh-
Who are you?

HUFF ハア

HUFF ハア

HUFF ハア

Ah! Oh,
yeah! Ah
ha ha!

I'll just
take off
my
makeup.

SPLASH
ざぶ

SPLASH
ざぶ

N--
Nana?

A
little
cautious. →

.....

Yup?

If Shôhei-
chan hadn't
been up
there, I
wouldn't
have made it
here.

It was
touch
and go
for a
bit!

Ha ha ha
ha!

You
made me
really
nervous.

I mean,
I'm glad
you
managed
to
transform.

Phew!
It's
"Nana."

That girl was Nana!!

YAAAAAH!!

Before conversion.

After conversion.

Her clothes...

That fan...

GRIN

Just that!

♡
♡

Did it hurt?

But my emotion is totally serious! I'm more jealous of you than you can imagine!

Wh-What's the deal...

Sorry to make it all red! Ah ha ha!

Wow!

...with this chick?!

Chapter 12
Something's Wrong With You

This is the dress I wore last night!

It was my favorite outfit!

How did it turn into this?!

Moriyama-kun!!

"I'm here for you!"

"Sorry. I'm in a hurry..."

Yo! Yaya!

POFF

Tell me! Whatever it is!

What's wrong? Did something happen?

.....Yeah...

Good morning!

He...

S-Sorry! It isn't that.

Is my voice that scary?

What's with the shocked face?

But congratulations!

I-Is that so?

The gig went really well!

I was so nervous about it, I blurted out that you didn't have to come. But I regretted it later.

I wanted to see it, but yesterday I was on the bridge...the Jingu-bashi, so...

...doesn't hate me!!

Once the term exams are over, it's summer vacation, huh?

It's time to stop being so worried!

Besides, I don't want Moriyama to get sick of me.

2-B

Uh... It's a little late in the term, but...

...from today on, our class is bigger by one person.

KLNCH
ﾄﾞｩｯ...

What's with that girl?

Why's she so close to him?

BOW

I'm Megumi Hano! The only thing to recommend me is that I've got lots of energy!

It's nice to meet you all!

Oh, you know each other?

You're kidding! Moriyama-kun?!

Hano-chan?!

SKRCH

WHISPER WHISPER WHISPER WHISPER

Just as I thought that she was the cutest thing...

...suddenly Moriyama swoops in and steals her away!

"I think you have the wrong club."

It's that girl from last night.

Yes!

Wow! What a coincidence, huh?

♪

She was so nice!

I'm fine!

She's a fun girl, huh?

Did she tire you out?

She's a one-girl riot, huh?

.....

...your friendship is just a school-*only* thing?

Oh, then...

But I've never seen you at any of his gigs.

You and Moriyama-kun look like you're very close.

STAB

That may be true...

Yeah, it's just never worked out.

Y-You think so?

Yesterday this big fashion hog of a guy tried to pick me up!

Oh, yeah! Listen to this!

Isn't it just so annoying when guys try to pick you up when you're just walking through town?

I turned him down, of course!

JIKK

I've got a bad feeling...

Ohhh! I know!

That'd be nice! Why not?

EHHHH?!

WORN OUT.

I've hardly ever had guys try to pick me up.

But you've found a way to disinterest all boys! I'm going to have to try that!

♡
You learn something new every day!

Why would they when Yaya walks through town, head down, like the world is coming to an end!!

NOOOOOO!!

イ ネ ネ ネ ネ ー !

ぶ す ー ッ
SSSSTABB

This is an expressionistic image?
※イメージ映像です

If you don't read it, Justice will be done!!
The huge hit series running in *Bessatsu Friend*!!
Hano-chan has set herself up as Nana's enemy, and she begins to show just how much of an underhanded enemy she can be!! Can Nana's "Justice" take down such an explosive rival?! And how will the Yaya=Nana equation play out with Moriyama and Shôhei??
You won't be able to turn your eyes away!!
In the next Othello Volume 4!!

About the Author

Satomi Ikezawa's previous work before *Othello* is *Guru Guru Pon-chan*. She currently continues to work on *Othello*, which is being serialized in the Kodansha weekly manga magazine, *Bessatsu Friend*.
Ikezawa won the 24th Kodansha Manga Prize in 2000 for *Guru Guru Pon-chan*.
She has two Labradors, named Guts and Ponta.

Translation Notes

Japanese is a tricky language for most Westerners, and translation is often more art than science. For your edification and reading pleasure, here are notes on some of the places where we could have gone in a different direction in our translation of the work, or where a Japanese cultural reference is used.

Entrances to Yoyogi Park, Page 17

The easiest and quickest way to get into Yoyogi Park is the Harajuku Station, which is only a bridge-span away from the greenery. (Ironically, Yoyogi Station is farther away from Yoyogi Park than Harajuku Station.) However, one can get to the park by getting off the train at Shibuya Station (about a kilometer away), and walking north through downtown Shibuya, past the NHK building and

the National Gym, and finally reaching the park. A little roundabout, but doable.

Underage access to alcohol, Page 21

The Japanese police are excellent, and the conviction rate for arrests is above 90%. Maybe that's why the Japanese feel that it is safe to sell beer and other alcoholic beverages through unsupervised

vending machines found all over the country. To be fair, their trust (or teenagers' fear of arrest) seems to be well placed, because very few teenagers seem to take advantage of the readily available chance to break the law. Moriyama-kun may be an exception, though...

The Lunch Counter Battle, Page 28

Yep, it's true. A local bakery is contracted to come to the school, set up with sandwiches, buns, and other lunch items at a counter found somewhere on campus, and the battle begins. If bakeries bring enough food for all the

SQEEZ

I'm so hungry, but this battle is too rough!

students who want it, the battle is for the sandwiches with the best reputation. Katsu-sando, pork-cutlet sandwiches (see the notes in Othello Vol. 1), are usually the first to sell out. But some bakeries don't want to have any leftover stock, and so they send less than the students will demand, and therefore they sell out every day, at the price of leaving some students hungry.

Anpan buns, Page 29

A thick doughy bun with a very thin crust baked crisp. Filling a yeast pocket in the center of the bun is a sweet-bean paste named "an." It was first introduced on the Ginza in the 1870s (Meiji-era Japan) and has spread

out to be one of the most popular and inexpensive snacks in the country (usually costing around 100 yen). "Pan," taken from the Portuguese word, is the Japanese word for bread. For those familiar with the anime "Anpanman," the title character is so named because his head is the shape of an anpan bun.

Thank god, Page 29

The average Japanese person seems nonreligious, but most Japanese belong to two religions, Buddhism and Shintoism (giving Japan the odd statistic of having more members of religious organizations than they have population). However, like the common phrase in English, "Thank God," in Japanese religious observance it is common to thank the gods (a Shinto god or gods in Yaya's case) when something miraculous happens.

Best (blank) in all Japan, Page 43

We all want to know where to get the best cheesesteak in Philadelphia, the best deep-dish pizza in Chicago, or the poshest restaurant in New York City. Japan takes this even further with well-known rankings for nearly everything. The best university (for example) is Tokyo University—regardless of your area of study—and everyone knows it. Kitamura-ya in our manga is only one character different from the real-life shop that baked the very first anpan, Kimura-ya in the Ginza, so it isn't that hard to figure out where to go for anpan the next time you hit the Ginza for shopping.

Roman Letters for Japanese, Page 44

There are three official sets of characters in the Japanese language: kanji, hiragana and katakana—but one other set of characters is in common usage: our alphabet, which we inherited from the Roman Empire. This is called Roma-ji ("Roman characters") in Japan, and since it is not an official character set, romaji has many conflicting rules when it is used to represent Japanese. Most of the variations in rules occur with sounds that are represented by more than one letter (such as the "sh" sound found in the syllable "shi," which can be represented as"shi," "syi," or just "si") or by sounds that aren't distinguished in English (such as the long

"o" sound which can be represented as "ou," "oo," "ô," "oh," or simply, "o"). Until the Japanese government weighs in on this issue, we will just have to expect inconsistent spelling when the Japanese (or translators) use romaji.

Hana Ichi Monme, Page 76

A children's game similar to Red Rover, where two lines of children face each other and try to entice members of the opposite line over to their line while singing the Hana Ichi Monme nursery-school song.

Nanameikan, Page 116

"Nanameikan" as a name for a club is something of a pun. The Rokumeikan (Cry of the Deer House) was a huge Victorian-style mansion constructed in the 1880s for the purpose of entertaining foreign dignitaries. It became a symbol of the Westernization of Japan. But since "roku" in Japanese means not only "deer" but also "six" (and one meaning for "nana" is "seven") you get a cute name for a goth club.

Yellow Card/Red Card, Page 150

For those people in the world who are not soccer-crazy, the yellow card is a warning given to a player after an egregious foul. When the red card (two yellows equals one red) is given after an especially dangerous foul, the player is thrown out of the game, and the team must play short-handed for the rest of the match.

NEGIMA!™

BY KEN AKAMATSU

Negi Springfield is a ten-year-old wizard teaching English at an all-girls Japanese school. He dreams of becoming a master wizard like his legendary father, the Thousand Master. At first his biggest concern was concealing his magic powers, because if he's ever caught using them publicly, he thinks he'll be turned into an ermine! But in a world that gets stranger every day, it turns out that the strangest people of all are Negi's students! From a librarian with a magic book to a centuries-old vampire, from a robot to a ninja, Negi will risk his own life to protect the girls in his care!

Ages: 16+

Special extras in each volume! Read them all!

BY JIN KOBAYASHI

SUBTLETY IS FOR WIMPS!

She . . . is a second-year high school student with a single all-consuming question: Will the boy she likes ever really notice her?

He . . . is the school's most notorious juvenile delinquent, and he's suddenly come to a shocking realization: He's got a huge crush, and now he must tell her how he feels.

Life-changing obsessions, colossal foul-ups, grand schemes, deep-seated anxieties, and raging hormones—School Rumble portrays high school as it really is: over-the-top comedy!

Ages: 13+

Special extras in each volume! Read them all!

Guru Guru Pon-Chan

RUFF RUFF LIFE

Ponta is a Labrador retriever puppy, the Koizumi family's pet. She's full of energy and usually up to some kind of mischief. But when Grandpa Koizumi, an amateur inventor, creates the Guru Guru Bone, Ponta's curiosity causes trouble. She nibbles the bone—and turns into a human girl!

Surprised but undaunted, Ponta ventures out of the house and meets Mirai Iwaki, the most popular boy at school. When Mirai saves her from a speeding car, Ponta changes back into her puppy self. Yet much has changed for Ponta during her short adventure as a human. Her heart races and her face flushes when she thinks of Mirai now. She's in love! Using the power of the Guru Guru Bone, Ponta switches back and forth from dog to girl—but can she win Mirai's affections?

Ages: 13+

Winner of the Kodansha Manga of the Year Award!

Includes special extras after the story!

It's hard to resist Cyan: he's an adorable catboy, whose cute ears and tail have made him a beloved pet. But then his family abandons him, leaving the innocent Cyan to fend for himself.

Just when Cyan thinks he's all alone in the world, he meets the Free Collars, a cool gang of stray cats who believe that no feline should allow a human to imprison his Wild Spirit. They invite Cyan to join them, and the reluctant housecat has to decide fast, because a rival gang of cats is threatening the Free Collars' territory! Can Cyan learn to free his Wild Spirit—and help his new friends save their home?

TAKUYA FUJIMA

Ages 16+

Special extras in each volume! Read them all!

idea

Library Learning Information

Idea Store® Canary Wharf
Churchill Place
Canary Wharf
London E14 5RB

020 7364 4332
www.ideastore.co.uk

Created and managed
by Tower Hamlets Council

THAT'S RIGHT! AUTHENTIC MANGA IS READ THE TRADITIONAL JAPANESE WAY—FROM RIGHT TO LEFT. EXACTLY THE OPPOSITE OF HOW ENGLISH BOOKS ARE READ. IT'S EASY TO FOLLOW: JUST GO TO THE OTHER END OF THE BOOK, AND READ EACH PAGE—AND EACH PANEL—FROM THE RIGHT SIDE TO THE LEFT SIDE, STARTING AT THE TOP RIGHT. NOW YOU'RE EXPERIENCING MANGA AS IT WAS MEANT TO BE.